WHAT TO LOOK FOR WHEN
LOOKING FOR A WIG

BY JEANNA DOYLE

FOR PAM DOW

WIG ED

WHAT TO LOOK FOR WHEN
LOOKING FOR A WIG

BY JEANNA DOYLE

*Wig ED* shall serve as an information resource only and is not to be used or relied upon for any diagnostic or treatment purposes. The ideas and suggestions contained within these pages should be used with discretion and are not intended to serve as a substitute for seeking advice, counseling, diagnosis, treatment or other intervention from a qualified medical professional or counselor. Neither the author nor publisher are engaged in rendering psychological, medical or any type of professional advice to readers; neither author nor publisher should be considered liable or responsible for any injury or damage allegedly arising from any information or suggestion presented in this book, including but not limited to physical, psychological, emotional, financial or other commercial loss. Readers should consult with a health care provider before making any health care decisions or for guidance about a specific medical condition.

Published in the United States by Books Ruhl, LLC
Printed in the U.S.A.

LIBRARY OF CONGRESS CONTROL NUMBER PENDING

ISBN 978-0-9981839-0-9

3

# WHO THIS
# BOOK IS FOR

*Wig ED* is for **you**,
women experiencing
hair loss

I think we can all agree that no matter what
the reason, hair loss sucks! Throughout
the book I reference the special needs of
women undergoing treatment for cancer and
women with alopecia areata. That said, there
is something in *Wig ED* for anyone seeking
advice on selecting a wig.

As I worked on the research for *Wig ED*, it became clear to me that there is not enough being done for women experiencing hair loss. Yet statistics* show that there are tens of millions of women experiencing hair loss. Therefore, in addition to providing advice on how to select a wig, my hope is that *Wig Ed* will start a conversation, one with, for, and about women affected by hair loss; a conversation that will increase both awareness and acceptance. My goal is to shift the public perception of women wearing wigs from "she's sick" to "she's stylish."

My goal is to shift the public perception of women wearing wigs from "she's sick" to "she's stylish."

If it's privacy you seek *Wig ED* provides you tools to keep your wig wearing your secret. But I believe you should be free to experiment with being bald one day and blonde or brunette the next. Please join me in this conversation at www.wiged.com. I'm certain that by raising our voices together we can raise a few hairs.

Here now is *Wig ED*. Conversation started...

*page 118

# ADVICE ON HOW TO READ THIS BOOK

Breathe.

If you are reading this book because it's 3:00 o'clock in the morning, you can't sleep, your hair is falling out from chemo, and you want a wig tomorrow, first, my prayers are with you. Second, it bears repeating: breathe. I am here to walk you through this journey. Want a wig immediately? Skip to Chapter 2: Hairy Tales. This chapter has everything you need to know to pick out a believable-looking wig (or two). Come back at your leisure and read the rest. Throughout the book there are charts to help summarize key information. Finished with Chapters 1 through 7? Check out the appendix for stories, statements, and statistics you won't want to miss.

NOW SIT BACK, RELAX, AND GET
YOUR WIG EDUCATION ON.

— Your Fairy Wigmother

# TABLE of CONTENTS

*She took a deep breath*
*and let it go...*

~ Author Unknown

# CHAPTER ONE

**MAN VS MACHINE**
HUMAN OR SYNTHETIC

**SET** aside any preconceived notions you may have about human hair wigs versus synthetic wigs, as well as the idea that unless you spend a fortune on your wig it will look terrible, or worse, like you're wearing a wig. I'm happy to tell you that is simply not true. As you learn what matters most in a wig you can stretch your dollar with confidence.

Consider how often you'll be rocking your wig and how long you'll wear it each time. These factors are important as you decide whether to go with a synthetic wig, or a human hair wig (or a blend–a combination of the two). Human hair wigs are typically more expensive than synthetic hair wigs. Expensive materials and higher prices are generally associated with a better quality product, but in the world of wigs, sometimes your best choice also happens to be less expensive! The key is knowing the strengths and drawbacks of the different types of construction and materials. With this knowledge in hand you can easily find a believable, cost-effective solution without wrecking your wallet.

All the wigs photographed in
this book are less than $100.

**INSURANCE**

Before we begin, here is some important information about wigs and insurance coverage. The cost of your wig, whether human or synthetic, when designated as a medical prosthesis, can be reimbursed at up to 100% (you'll need your physician to write you a prescription). Even if your insurance doesn't provide coverage for a "cranial prosthesis" (that's medical terminology for a wig), you may still be able to claim it as a medical tax deduction, provided you retain your receipt and the prescription from your doctor.

### HUMAN HAIR

If you are experiencing the permanent hair loss associated with alopecia areata, you may want to consider a human hair wig. Due to the labor-intensive manufacturing process and the natural materials used, human hair wigs cost more. But the additional cost will be amortized over time, as these wigs will last longer than synthetics when worn continuously over an extended period. A well-made human hair wig feels and responds more like natural hair; however, it will, like your own hair, need to be styled more frequently, as it will be affected by humidity, rain, and perspiration.

With proper care, a human hair wig will last approximately 12 months. This varies according to factors such as exposure to heat, friction due to wearing a hat, and how well the wig is cared for. If you want a custom-made human hair wig, seek a shop that can help you find your perfect measurements. However, many manufacturers have human hair options that you may purchase and wear the same day.

### REMY HAIR

Considered the "Cadillac" of human hair, Remy hair feels smooth and luxurious. With Remy hair the cuticles are intact and flow in the same direction, making it more manageable (and more expensive).

### COMBINATION HUMAN AND SYNTHETIC HAIR, OR BLENDS

Wigs that combine both synthetic and human hair offer the best of both worlds. A blend of human and synthetic hair provides the ease of maintenance of synthetic hair with the added believability of a human hair wig. This combination will cost slightly more than synthetic-only, but far less than a full human hair wig.

**Note:** Throughout the book I will reference both synthetic and human hair. If blended hair is not mentioned, follow instructions for human hair. Also, when you see the term "Blend," I'm referring to a wig that is a blend, in varying proportions, of human and synthetic hair.

HUMAN HAIR

## SYNTHETIC HAIR

Whether you want a wig for temporary hair loss or simply for a change of style, a synthetic wig is an affordable yet effective option. A synthetic wig's style is locked in, so the wig will not lose its shape when washed. A wide variety of styles and finishes are available, with multiple color options that would take time and money to achieve in a salon. However, with a quick trip to the wig shop, these qualities are yours for the wearing. Synthetic wigs generally need to be replaced after three to six months of frequent wear, as they are typically made of acrylic, plastic, or polyvinyl, which break down with friction (caused by things like frequently brushing against clothes, or from hot or cold temperatures). This makes the ends look damaged and the hair hard to comb through. However, by that time, you may be ready to try a new style.

**Note:** Synthetic wigs, unless otherwise labeled, cannot withstand heat well and may even singe. Consequently, be careful when blowing out candles, opening oven doors, manning barbecues, or unloading steamy dishwashers. There are some types of synthetic fibers that can hold up to low heat settings on curling irons and blow dryers. Look for the term "heat resistant" or "heat friendly" but beware; there are varying degrees of heat resistance and with each degree, the price goes up. Not only will you pay more to have these styling options, but you'll miss out on one of the biggest advantage of a synthetic wig–the convenience of a ready-to-wear hairstyle.

SYNTHETIC HAIR

*Fear is excitement
without the breath.*

~ Fritz Perls

# CHAPTER TWO

**HAIRY TALES**

FIVE TIPS SO YOUR DREAM LOOK DOESN'T
BECOME A NIGHTMARE, PLUS A HINT OF COLOR

**AHH** the fairy tales of our youth. So many of us cherish the fanciful stories passed down for generations about the magical allure of beautiful hair. Be it golden, raven, long, or lustrous, we all have a dream hair checklist. It's only natural to imagine having those wishes finally fulfilled on your wig-shopping quest, but be forewarned. Some of those dream qualities can be a real nightmare in a wig. Follow these five tips (to achieve a fairytale ending).

# THE
## FANTASY

*YOU WILL FEEL YOUNG, BEAUTIFUL
AND SEXY WITH A WIG THAT'S:*

LONG | THICK | STRAIGHT
SHINY | SOLID COLOR

$\longrightarrow$

# THE
## REALITY

*YOU WILL MORE*
*LIKELY FEEL:*

HOT | TIRED | UNCOMFORTABLE
FRUSTRATED | SELF-CONSCIOUS

Fear not, my darlings! If you have your heart set on one
or more of these qualities (long, thick, straight, shiny, or
solid color), there are tips in the pages ahead to help you
and your wig live happily ever after.

# A Long Wig

LONG CONSIDERED ONE OF THE
MOST DESIRABLE AND SOUGHT
AFTER QUALITIES FOR HAIR, MANY
OF US WILL GO TO GREAT LENGTHS
**[LITERALLY]** TO ACQUIRE LONG
LOCKS. HOWEVER, IN A WIG, THIS
QUALITY FALLS SHORT.

# DRAWBACKS TO A LONG WIG

### SYNTHETIC HAIR

Remember that you are wearing man-made fibers. Despite how far manufacturing has come, it is not real hair and will not respond in the same manner as real hair; the longer the hair, the heavier and hotter the wig. If you are not used to the weight of a wig, you'll be surprised to discover that it weighs more than natural hair (especially since you'll probably often wear both a wig and a wig cap). Just like wearing a hat for extended periods of time, wigs also hold in a lot of heat, which can give you a headache.

### HUMAN HAIR/BLENDS

Most of the same drawbacks of a long synthetic hair wig also apply to a long human hair wig. Long human hair wigs are less of a problem than long synthetic wigs when in contact with clothing, but they will still tangle.

**Suggestion:** For the reasons stated above, whether synthetic or human, I suggest you choose a wig length that rests just above (but not touching) your shoulders. It will be cooler, lighter, and far more manageable.

## STILL NOT CONVINCED AND WANT A LONG WIG ANYWAY?

Here are some tips to keep your wig-wearing experience from coming up short.

### SYNTHETIC HAIR, HUMAN HAIR, & BLENDS

If you desire a long wig, try one with layers. This will reduce both the weight and heat. Prefer all one length? Have a professional wig cutter remove some of the bulk without changing its length. This can make a long wig feel noticeably lighter (for tips on finding a professional wig cutter, see Chapter 5). Avoid excess hair spray or sticky products that may make the hair grab the back of your clothes or cause static.

### SYNTHETIC HAIR

For help with comfort and manageability, try the following customization: If you like DIY projects and you are handy with a needle and thread, this is a project you can do yourself. Not interested in another project? This same modification can be made by a wig professional. Most stores carry human hair sewn on single tracks that hang down vertically and are typically used to add thickness or length to one's natural hair. Place one or two of these tracks, depending on the thickness you desire, on the underside at the base of your wig and secure with a few basting stitches. The tracks should extend down the full length of your wig. The tracks will not be visible, as they are underneath the existing hair of the wig, but they provide a buffering layer that feels nicer against the back of your neck. They also lessen the tendency of long synthetic hair to tangle when in direct contact with clothing.

### HUMAN HAIR / BLENDS

Keep human hair wigs and blended hair wigs clean and dry, as styling products and dampness can add weight to the wig.

### TRY TWO STYLES

If you wear your synthetic wig daily, you will likely need to replace it after three to six months. Since synthetics are relatively inexpensive, consider picking up a long and a mid-length wig. With both lengths to choose from, you can be long on style without being short on comfort.

# A NOTE ABOUT HAIR LOSS DUE TO CHEMOTHERAPY

If you are experiencing sudden hair loss from chemotherapy and are accustomed to long hair, remember, this is only temporary. Most likely, when you have enough coverage from regrowth of your own hair, you'll no longer want to wear a wig. At this time, you will have a short style until your hair reaches your desired length. When the hair sheds, the scalp may become tender, so it's best to avoid the heat and friction from wearing a long wig.

# A Straight Wig

STRAIGHT HAIR HAS BEEN COVETED BY
MANY SINCE THE BEGINNING OF TIME
AND HAS INSPIRED BOTH PRODUCTS
AND APPLIANCES TO HELP US LAND
THIS LOOK.

## DRAWBACKS OF A STRAIGHT WIG, (SYNTHETIC, HUMAN, OR BLENDS)

The part and the hairline are the two main areas to consider to keep believability high. With straight wigs, when the hair lies flat, the part is exposed. Depending on the cut, the hairline can be more visible as well. There are some wigs that work better than others if you want a style that has a noticeable part or if you want to wear your hair back off your face, exposing your hairline. These options are covered in Chapter 4.

Natural hair generally has subtle variations in color and texture.

For example, the ends may be thinner and lighter in natural hair, while the fibers of synthetic wigs are man-made and lack the naturally occurring variations of human hair. The straighter the fiber, the more perfect the ends look, making it more apparent that you are wearing a wig.

**Suggestion:** For added believability, try a wig with some soft curls to help draw attention away from the part and hairline. Additionally, subtle variations in color can also provide a more natural, less uniform look.

## STILL NOT CONVINCED AND WANT A STRAIGHT WIG ANYWAY?

In both synthetic and human hair, look for a wig with some layering throughout the crown. Layering will give you the straight hair you seek while preventing overly uniform hair length, which can result in a less natural look. You might also want to look for something with a point cut. A point cut is a style where the ends are cut at an angle, making them lighter and offering better movement; this is in contrast to a blunt cut, where the ends are cut straight across and lay flat.

# A Thick Wig

THICK HAIR LOOKS HEALTHY AND YOUTHFUL. MANY OF US SPEND AN EXTRAVAGANT AMOUNT OF TIME AND MONEY IN PURSUIT OF MORE VOLUME – THINK BLOW DRYERS, CURLING IRONS, SHAMPOOS, AND STYLING PRODUCTS. HOWEVER, WHEN CHOOSING A WIG, IT'S WISE TO DE-BULK THIS DESIRE. READ ON FOR ATTRACTIVE ALTERNATIVES.

## DRAWBACKS OF A THICK WIG, (SYNTHETIC, HUMAN, OR BLENDS)

Thick wigs are less comfortable. A thick wig will be hot because its density blocks air flow, and the weight of all that hair can quickly grow tiresome.

In addition, if you have temporary or permanent hair loss, it's likely that your eyebrows and eyelashes have also thinned and will contrast with a thick wig.

**Suggestion:** As an alternative, try a wig with a light wave. Waves create the appearance of greater volume while being able to avoid the discomfort of a thick wig.

## STILL NOT CONVINCED AND WANT A THICK WIG ANYWAY?

You can fulfill your fantasy of volume without resorting to a hot, heavy wig. Start with a wig that has some layering at the crown and hair that has lift at the top of the wig (as opposed to one designed to lay flat). This will provide a look of added volume. You can also try some teasing near the crown using a pick-style comb. Tease the hair, then smooth out any loops or rough edges using the pick side of the comb, then add a little hairspray. The result will be a fuller look with wide appeal.

# A Shiny Wig

SHINY HAIR, SKIN, OR NAILS ARE
ASSOCIATED WITH YOUTHFUL
RADIANCE. CONSEQUENTLY, A
SEA OF BEAUTY PRODUCTS HAVE
FLOODED THE MARKET TO HELP
US ACHIEVE MORE SPARKLE.

# DRAWBACKS OF A SHINY WIG

### SYNTHETIC HAIR

In a synthetic wig, the fibers are manufactured and have a more uniform look. High shine in a synthetic wig looks artificial; ultimately, it is less convincing than one with a more matte-looking finish. Although most synthetic wigs will become less shiny with wear, why wait? Choose one with a more natural finish from the start.

### HUMAN HAIR

Most human hair wigs use the strong, thick, and shiny hair found in people of Asian, East Indian, or Eastern European descent.

This human hair, once it has been processed, can look even shinier. If you have naturally thinner or softer hair, this extra shine may look unnatural.

**Suggestion:** A wig with a more matte, natural finish is a better choice versus one with a high shine. If your wig is a bit too shiny, you can lessen the shine by applying a little spray-on dry shampoo. You can also try gently rubbing the outer portion of an overly shiny wig with a soft t-shirt (test this on the underside of the wig first).

## STILL NOT CONVINCED AND WANT A SHINY WIG ANYWAY?

If you long for luster, a smart approach is to start with a wig that's shy on the shiny side. You can add some shine selectively with products like a shine spray or gel. When applying a shine-enhancing product, be careful to avoid the crown of the wig; rather, only apply the product to the middle and ends. You can achieve a more realistic look by varying the degree of shine you add.

# A Solid Color Wig

BE IT BLONDE, RED, OR RAVEN,

A CASCADE OF SOLID COLOR

CAN OFFER A DRAMATIC AND

STRIKING LOOK.

# DRAWBACKS OF A SOLID-COLOR WIG (SYNTHETIC, HUMAN, OR BLENDS)

For both synthetic and human hair wigs, a natural look is key. A wig with an overall solid color may not be as believable as its multi-hued counterpart.

**Suggestion:** Select instead the color you like but with slight variations in hue. This can take the form of traditional highlights throughout the wig. Alternatively, it can consist of a darker base at the crown (referred to as rooted colors), which is similar to the conventional growing-out process of your natural hair when colored. Some wigs are designed to be a bit darker underneath from ear to ear, with lighter highlights around the face. These variations in hue and tone are incorporated because they add dimension and authenticity. Creating these looks at a salon would result in an expensive bill, but they're gratis when they come with your wig.

**Note:** If your natural hair is very dark and one-toned, you may wish to select a wig with less dimension or no additional colors. Try on several solid-color and multi-shaded wigs to determine the option you prefer. As you try on wigs with varying degrees of color, keep in mind which ones best match your skin, taking into consideration any changes that may be occurring due to treatment or illness.

## STILL NOT CONVINCED AND WANT A SOLID-COLOR WIG ANYWAY?

Go ahead and go blonde, redhead, or brunette. Look for a wig in the glamorous color of your choice but with subtle tonal variations: either gentle highlights or subtle darker lowlights. The resulting realism of one color with differing tones rather than a solid, unvaried color will be pure magic.

## A NOTE FOR PERSONS RECEIVING CHEMOTHERAPY

If your hair color is dark and cool-toned and you are experiencing chemo-related skin changes along with hair loss, try a dark wig color similar to your own hair but with lighter, warm highlights (such as a copper shade). This strategy will result in an overall hair color that is more flattering to your complexion and will help to offset the temporary changes in the appearance of your skin.

# TIPS *ON* COLOR

I ALWAYS SUGGEST THAT MY CLIENTS SHOP NAKED
(OR WEARING AS LITTLE FOUNDATION AS POSSIBLE)
SO THEY CAN SEE HOW THE WIG COLOR LOOKS NEXT
TO THEIR SKIN. YOU CAN ADJUST YOUR MAKEUP
BUT THE WIG'S COLOR IS A CONSTANT. I ALSO
RECOMMEND LOOKING AT THE WIG IN NATURAL
DAYLIGHT FOR COLOR ACCURACY. TRY ON WIGS THAT
ARE SLIGHTLY WARMER AND LIGHTER, AS THEY MAY
BE MORE FLATTERING TO SKIN THAT IS UNDERGOING
CHANGES. REMEMBER, THERE MAY BE DAYS WHEN
YOU'LL WANT TO WEAR YOUR WIG WITH LITTLE OR
NO MAKEUP. IT MAY BE WORTHWHILE TO STEP OUT OF
YOUR COMFORT ZONE AND TEST A VARIETY OF NEW
HUES TO ENSURE YOU FIND YOUR BEST LOOK. MANY
MANUFACTURERS MAKE THE SAME STYLE IN SEVERAL
SHADES, SO DON'T BE SHY ABOUT ASKING TO SEE THE
FULL RANGE OF COLOR OPTIONS.

# HAIRY TALES

# 5
# TIPS
*(plus one)*

| | DRAWBACK | SUGGESTION | WORKAROUND |
|---|---|---|---|
| **LONG WIG** | Heavy | Shoulder length or above | Add layers for a lighter feel |
| **STRAIGHT WIG** | Too uniform-looking | A little wave | Light layers to break up the crown and part |
| **THICK WIG** | Hot, thickness does not match thinning eyebrows | Curls or waves to give the look of volume | A crown with lift, and add strategic teasing |
| **SHINY WIG** | Unnatural looking | Matte finish or more natural finish | Add selective shine to a few areas |
| **SOLID COLOR WIG** | Lacks dimension | A darker crown or multiple toned highlights | Solid shade with tonal variations like highlights and lowlights |

*Color:* Choose a color while wearing very little foundation in order to find the best color for your skin tone. A wig with highlights and low lights offers added dimension and believability.

*Eat. Breathe, Sleep. For now, just breathe.*

~ Abigail Mattson*

# CHAPTER THREE

## THE BIG BANG THEORY
### HOW TO GET MORE BANG FOR YOUR BUCK

**FOR** many of us, bangs have long been the bane of our existence. To cut or not to cut? We can all remember those tedious periods of trying to grow bangs out while we decide what to do with them. Somehow, we forget those struggles when we have all-one-length hair; we get bored and want a change, and therefore, end up repeating the entire process.

*Abigail Mattson shares her feelings upon being diagnosed with cancer. To see Abigail's full message, available in nine languages, go to www.suitehope.org/translatinghope.

# THE MOST BANG FOR YOUR BUCK

A wig with bangs offers a high rate of return in the categories of finance and believability. Bangs offer forgiveness around the hairline – the main area to conceal for the most natural of looks. As a bonus, with wigs, bangs do not require frequent trips to the salon for trimming, and can also deflect focus from thinning eyebrows and forehead wrinkles.

# BANGS MAKE US
# *CRAZY*

Typically bangs make us crazy because they are only the perfect length for about one week of every haircut cycle. Too long before cutting, too short right after, briefly just right, then back to too long again, and repeat. But in a wig, bangs are always Goldilocks perfect. Imagine having bangs at your ideal length for as long as you have the wig, with no awkward growing-out phases!

So whether you want partial, full, thick, thin, side-swept, or forward-facing bangs, they will not only conceal the hairline, but also help to frame the face. Whatever your bang preference, there is a style to fulfill your dreams.

Look for a wig with bangs that are comfortable near your eyes or glasses, and that complement your look without requiring a lot of management. You may fall in love with more than one style and consider taking several home. Think of your wig as a wardrobe accessory.

# Consider the different type of cuts and what effect each offers:

Blunt-cut bangs are cut level from side to side with the hair designed to be combed straight forward. They typically lay flat.

Point-cut bangs provide a lighter, barely there look. They can be swept to the side and are designed to impart a feathery quality.

**Not seeing what you want?** Wigs can be professionally cut to adjust the bangs to suit your face perfectly. Read more on professional wig cutters in Chapter 5: Shear Perfection.

*Smile, breathe,*
*and go slowly.*

~ Thich Nhat Hanh

# CHAPTER FOUR

GETTIN' WIGGY WITH IT
THE 411 ON CONSTRUCTION

**IN** the world of wigs, there are four main categories of wig cap construction, and many variations within each category. Information about wig construction is often dry and technical, and does little to answer important questions like: "How does this help me choose a wig?" Never fear. This chapter will help you answer the important questions of function and style while offering an overview of these four construction types. Now you can land a look that will make you feel more styled than studied.

# CONSTRUCTION

# 1. Wefted

**THE STYLE:**

If you are looking for a low-maintenance style, a wig that is just wash-and-go, and if you don't mind that you can't change the style, try wefted construction. This construction is lightweight and offers good air circulation. With a wefted wig, in addition to the wig, you may want to wear a wig cap (typically made of nylon), which provides more comfort for sensitive scalps. The wefted wigs are typically the most affordable of all the construction types.

**THE STUDY:**

Wefted wigs are the most basic construction choice. Hair-like fibers are sewn in the same direction on thin ribbons of fabric throughout the entire wig, which enhances air circulation. Often the top of the wig is pre-teased at the base and throughout the crown, which helps to obstruct the view of the top of the wig, including the part, which is not designed to change. Check for a good fit. If the wefts are too far apart, the scalp may be exposed. Wefted wigs work great for short, layered, and curly hair looks.

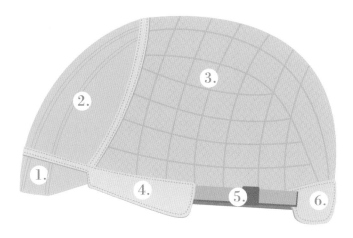

**WEFTED**

1. **Front Edge:** Solid Fabric (as shown above). With this construction, you may prefer bangs or a style that doesn't reveal the hairline. Alternately, lace front may be used in place of solid fabric for a more believable hairline.

2. **Crown:** Solid Fabric (as shown above). Hair in this area is typically pre-teased to keep visibility of the crown slightly obstructed. Alternately, monofilament may be used instead for comfort and a movable part.

3. **Body:** Open Wefted. This provides better ventilation.

4. **Ear Tabs:** Tabs to help level the wig. The tabs are bendable for slight adjustments to the fit (which is nice for eyeglass wearers).

5. **Adjustable Straps:** Used to tighten or loosen the wig. These can be bra-type hooks or Velcro® straps.

6. **Back Edge:** Bottom of the wig.

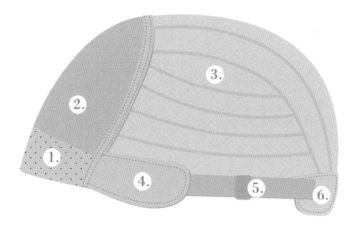

## MONOFILAMENT

1. **Front Edge:** Lace front construction (as shown above) provides a believable hairline. Alternatively, hair fibers may be sewn onto solid fabric, in which case you may prefer bangs or a style that doesn't reveal the hairline.

2. **Crown:** Monofilament, which allows multi-directional parting while providing the appearance of natural growth. This construction is more comfortable for bare skin.

3. **Body:** Open Wefted (as shown above). This provides for better ventilation. Alternatively, the body may be hand tied for ease of movement and more styling options.

4. **Ear Tabs:** Tabs to help level the wig. The tabs are bendable for slight adjustments to the fit (which is nice for eyeglass wearers).

5. **Adjustable Straps:** Used to tighten or loosen the wig. These can be bra-type hooks or Velcro® straps.

6. **Back Edge:** Bottom of the wig.

# 2. Monofilament

**THE STYLE:**

If you'd like to be able to change your part, monofilament tops and double monofilaments are great. For those experiencing hair loss due to chemotherapy, this may be a more comfortable choice, as this cap is softer against a sensitive scalp than the wefted construction. Monofilaments are durable and moderately priced compared to other wigs.

**THE STUDY:**

With monofilament top construction, the fibers or hairs are tied to an ultra-fine mesh of fabric that resembles the scalp. If you are seeking a style that shows the part this is a great option, as it will look the most natural. When shopping online you may see the following terms: monofilament crown, monofilament top, monofilament part, or double monofilament. These terms indicate the specific areas constructed with monofilament. While a wig with a monofilament crown only includes a small circle of monofilament at the crown (seen commonly in short wigs), a monofilament top has monofilament across the whole top of the wig, allowing you to change the location of your part. However, a monofilament part wig has a set part that cannot be moved from side to side. Double monofilament wigs have an extra layer of fabric to offer even greater comfort.

# 3. Lace Front

**THE STYLE:**

Do you like to push your hair back away from your face? Then look for a lace front wig. Lace front wigs are designed for the most natural-looking hairline possible. This is a great option for those who wish to go without bangs. Prices begin to rise with these flexible features.

**THE STUDY:**

Although it's called a lace front wig, it does not resemble lace in the traditional sense. The front portion of these wigs have fibers or hairs tied to the edges of a fine mesh that covers the hairline; some wigs only have this mesh across the temples, which allows for movement in this area. Other wigs have mesh from ear to ear for greater ease and movement. This construction makes it possible to move the hair freely when pinning your hair back or even just pushing the hair away from your face. Repairs may be required after extended wear; for such repairs, seek a wig professional. Chapter 6 has instructions on how to properly put on and take off your lace front wig. If you purchase a lace front wig from an online retailer, you will need to remove a small portion of the excess mesh material before wearing. Take a small pair of sewing scissors and trim the excess mesh along the perimeter, being careful not to cut into the hairline. The mesh is designed to disappear or blend seamlessly next to your skin, so don't worry if you can't make a precision cut; just go slow and try to keep it smooth, with no ragged edges. If you purchase it at a wig shop with an on-site professional, ask her (or him) to assist you.

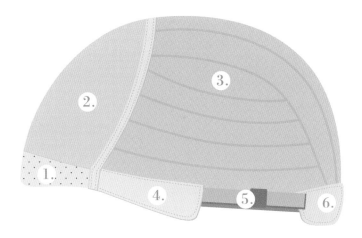

**LACE FRONT**

1. **Front Edge:** Lace front construction for a believable hairline and a style you can wear off of your face and with or without bangs.

2. **Crown:** Monofilament (as shown above), designed for comfort and a moveable part. Alternatively, the hair fibers may simply be sewn onto solid fabric, in which case the hair in this area is typically pre-teased to keep visibility of the crown slightly obstructed.

3. **Body:** Open Wefted (as shown above). This provides for better ventilation. Alternatively, the body may be hand tied for ease of movement and more styling options.

4. **Ear Tabs:** Tabs to help level the wig. The tabs are bendable for slight adjustments to the fit (which is nice for eyeglass wearers).

5. **Adjustable Straps:** Used to tighten or loosen the wig. These can be bra-type hooks or Velcro® straps.

6. **Back Edge:** Bottom of the wig.

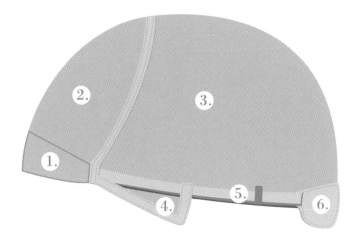

## HAND TIED

*1.*  **Front Edge:** Hand tied providing ease of movement and endless styling options.

*2.*  **Crown:** Hand tied providing ease of movement and endless styling options. The crown area may also have extra layers of fabric, such as double monofilament, to increase comfort for bare scalps.

*3.*  **Body:** Hand tied providing ease of movement and endless styling options.

*4.*  **Ear Tabs:** Tabs to help level the wig. The tabs are bendable for slight adjustments to the fit (which is nice for eyeglass wearers).

*5.*  **Adjustable Straps:** Used to tighten or loosen the wig. These can be bra-type hooks or Velcro® straps.

*6.*  **Back Edge:** Bottom of the wig.

# 4. Hand Tied

**THE STYLE:**

Hand tied wigs provide the most natural movement and look. While they feature the most luxurious construction, hand tied wigs are also quite a bit more expensive. If you're experiencing long-term hair loss, this type of wig may be worth considering, as you will be able to amortize the higher initial price tag over time. Bear in mind that these wigs will require regular care during their lifespan, whereas a less expensive wig could simply be replaced. If you would like to be able to play with lots of style options (like a ponytail or another type of updo style), this construction is ideal.

**THE STUDY:**

The term "fully hand knotted" refers to 100% hand tied construction. This is where you will see the Remy hair mentioned in Chapter 1, where the hair has the cuticles intact and it all flows in one direction. Due to the expensive natural materials and intensive labor required, the costs are high. *All* the hair or fibers are hand tied throughout the wig. Think of this wig as you would a beloved cashmere item. The initial price tag is higher and it requires a little extra care but offers major luxury, comfort, and style.

# A NOTE ABOUT CHEMOTHERAPY

If you are going through treatment, it's best not to use the adhesives (like tape or glue) used to help lace front wigs bond to your skin at the hairline. The glue can irritate sensitive skin and the fumes can cause the eyes to water, especially in cases where the eyelashes (which serve as a protective barrier) are shedding from treatment. Look instead for a lace front wig that works well without the need to glue the edges; there are many women who wear lace front wigs and don't use any adhesive at all.

# CONSTRUCTION OVERVIEW

## WEFTED WIGS

**BENEFIT**

most affordable

**FEATURES**

light weight,
low maintenance

## MONOFILAMENT WIGS

**BENEFIT**

comfortable against scalp

**FEATURES**

durable, resembles
natural part

## LACE FRONT WIGS

**BENEFIT**

believable hairline

**FEATURES**

can be worn off the face
or without bangs

## HAND TIED WIGS

**BENEFIT**

natural-looking

**FEATURES**

luxurious construction,
endless style options

# *SIZE*
# MATTERS

For most women, average-size wigs work fine, but if you've discovered when wearing hats that the "regular" sizes are too small or too large, check out the sizing chart on the opposite page to help you find your fairytale fit.

To determine your size, use a flexible tape measure (like one you'd use for measuring your waist). Beginning in front at your hairline, wrap it behind your ear, down to the nape of your neck, back up across the other ear, and finish at the starting point at your front hairline. Jot down the number and cross reference it with the chart provided.

Just like with shoes, where your size may vary from brand to brand, so too may your wig size. If ordering online, ask for advice on different manufacturers' sizing.

Remember, most wigs have a bra-type adjuster for fine tuning the fit. Also, a professional wig stylist can make small tweaks to help achieve a perfect fit.

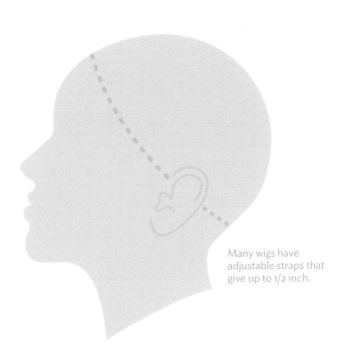

Many wigs have adjustable straps that give up to 1/2 inch.

| CAP SIZE | CIRCUMFERENCE |
|---|---|
| *Child/Ultra Petite* | *19 inches* |
| *Petite* | *21 inches* |
| *Petite/Average* | *21 ½ inches* |
| *Average/Large* | *22 inches* |
| *Large* | *23 inches* |

*Sizes may vary from manufacturer to manufacturer

*Happiness breathes
when you do.*

~ Terri Guillemets

# CHAPTER FIVE

**THE** relationship between a woman and her hairdresser is very often a friendship based on loyalty and trust. We value our stylist's opinion and share our deepest thoughts. In this light, it seems natural to ask them for help with a wig. However, while it may be a good idea to ask for an opinion on style and color, wig-cutting is an entirely different matter.

**Make it personal:** A professional wig cutter can be like your favorite seamstress, tailoring something off-the-rack into a perfect fit.

# WARNING:
## WIGS WON'T GROW BACK

CUTTING A WIG IS DRAMATICALLY
DIFFERENT THAN CUTTING NATURAL
HAIR. WHETHER YOU OPT FOR A
SYNTHETIC OR A HUMAN HAIR WIG,
SEEK A PROFESSIONAL STYLIST WHO
SPECIALIZES IN CUTTING WIGS. YOU
ONLY GET ONE SHOT AT GETTING THE
CUT RIGHT, BECAUSE (OBVIOUSLY)
UNLIKE HUMAN HAIR AFTER A MISHAP,
A WIG WILL NOT GROW BACK.

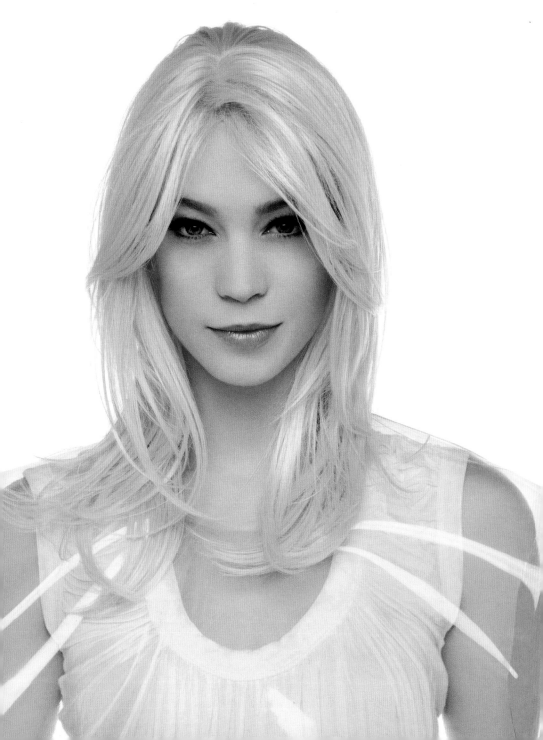

The things a professional wig cutter can do are shear magic. These wig wizards can custom-tailor a wig to your face. With just a snip here and there, they can tweak the bangs, or slightly shorten or thin your wig; even create the look of baby hair at the sides or nape of your wig for updos and ponytail styles, creating a true transformation. To find a professional wig cutter, look for a wig store that retains an on-site wig stylist. This customization is sometimes offered as a perk to clients who make a purchase; otherwise it's "a la carte." Either way, it is a service worth seeking. The same professionals can help you care for your wig over the life of the purchase. So, make your wig stylist a trusted new friend.

# HAVING AN ISSUE WITH YOUR WIG?

SEEK THE ADVICE OF A WIG EXPERT, AS THEY CAN OFFER A TAILORED SOLUTION JUST FOR YOU. MANY WIG STORES OFFER CLEANING, STYLING, AND REPAIR SERVICES FOR ALL TYPES OF WIGS, AND EVEN CUSTOM COLOR FOR HUMAN HAIR WIGS. ADDITIONALLY, WIG EXPERTS CAN MAKE ADJUSTMENTS TO YOUR WIG'S FIT.

*Breathe in, breathe out,*
*rinse and repeat.*

~ Your Fairy Wigmother

# CHAPTER SIX

**DON'T GET WIGGED OUT**

SIMPLE SOLUTIONS FOR WEAR, CARE & COMFORT

**WHETHER** for wind, water, workouts, or washing, here's some advice for you and your wig–from putting it on to pulling it off (with care, of course).

# CAUTION

If you have a hand tied or lace front wig, do not pull on the front or hairline, as you might stretch the fabric or pull out the hairs. Instead, using both of your hands, place them on either side of your temples, then move your hands back at least three inches from the front and gently lift up and move forward. Use this same technique to carefully remove the wig.

**FOR ADDED COMFORT:**

Unless your wig's built-in cap has been designed for maximum comfort, as with the double monofilament wig, consider wearing a wig cap. The wig cap is a finely woven nylon fabric cap that aids in the fit of the wig by keeping your hair in place; it offers a buffer between you and the wig.

# HOW TO PUT ON YOUR WIG

1. Pick up your wig, holding the tabs on either side. Once the wig is on, these tabs will be just in front of your ears. Now turn the wig upside down so you are looking at the inside of the wig.

2. Looking at the label in the back and still holding the tabs, position the front of the wig at your hairline just covering the front edge of the wig cap, and place it on your head.

3. Pull down on the back of the wig so it fits well at the nape of your neck.

4. Find the tabs again and make sure they have not slipped and are still lined up evenly with both ears. (Some wig styles have center parts and others part slightly off-center.) Checking the placement of the tabs at either side of your ears will confirm that you have positioned the wig correctly.

5. A tale-tale sign you are wearing a wig is that the hairline in the front of the wig is too low on your forehead or it sits too far back. Be sure to check that the front of the wig lines up with your natural hairline. If you are worried about the wig slipping, there are adjusters in the back to make the wig fit more securely. There's more on fit ahead in this chapter (see the section "For Added Security").

# HOW OFTEN DO I WASH MY WIG?

FREQUENCY OF WASHING IS A PERSONAL PREFERENCE AND DEPENDS ON FACTORS SUCH AS HOW OFTEN YOU WEAR THE WIG AND ITS EXPOSURE TO PERSPIRATION AND ODORS.

# WASHING YOUR
# SYNTHETIC WIG

**1.** Using a wide-tooth comb, comb through the wig, removing any tangles. If you prefer to use a brush, choose one that is well-vented (a brush with bristles that are not too close together). Do not brush a wet wig as it will cause damage and excess shedding.

**2.** Fill a sink with cool water.

**3.** Wash the wig with any type of shampoo.

**4.** Rinse well. Do not wring out.

**5.** Empty the sink and fill again with cool water.

**6.** Add a capful of conditioner and dip the wig. This will help reduce static. (Alternately, you can use a leave-in spray-on conditioner.)

**Caution:** Do not soak a hand tied or lace front wig. Soaking can create tangles and cause the hair to come loose and shed. Instead, dip the wig to rinse. Conditioner can also cause hand tied hair to loosen. Use the leave-in spray-on conditioner mentioned above, being careful not to saturate the crown or lace front area.

**Tip:** Wash your wig at night so it is ready to wear on the following day.

7. Rinse with cool water.

8. Blot away wetness with a towel and shake the wig out. If it is a short or curly wig, hang it upside down in the shower to dry.

9. If you would like to place it on a stand and let it air-dry, the stand should be smaller than your head; I often use a can of hairspray to prevent stretching out the wig. Use a wide-tooth comb to gently comb from top to bottom to remove any tangles.

**Note:** The synthetic wig is a wonderful wash and wear option. See the manufacturer's washing instructions.

## PRODUCT KNOWLEDGE – SYNTHETIC WIGS:

Cold water-soluble products are recommended and can be purchased when you buy the wig. Start with a small amount, because unlike human hair, synthetics can't absorb product. Then, the next time you style your wig, begin by adding a little water in the form of a spray or just directly with your fingers. This moisture will reactivate the existing product and you may find there's no need to add any more.

# WASHING YOUR HUMAN HAIR AND BLEND WIG

1. Using a wide-tooth comb, comb through the wig, removing any tangles. If you prefer to use a brush, choose one that is well-vented (a brush with bristles that are not too close together). Do not brush a wet wig, as it will cause damage and excess shedding.

2. Fill a sink with cool water.

3. Wash the wig with a mild shampoo free of sulfates and parabens, such as a baby shampoo or shampoo for color-treated hair. Note: If you have product build-up or excessive perspiration, use a clarifying shampoo, but use sparingly, as it can alter the finish of the wig.

4. Rinse well with cool water. Do not wring out.

5. Do not soak a human hair or blend wig. Soaking can cause tangles and hair loss. Use a leave-in spray-on conditioner to prevent loosening or weighing down the hair.

6. Blot the wig dry with a towel.

7. Place on a stand and let the wig air-dry. Just as with a synthetic wig, the stand should be smaller than your head. If you want smoother ends, let the wig dry to about 80% and then, using a couple of t-pins, secure the wig to a "head" form. Using a blow-dryer set at the low heat setting, dry the wig the remaining 20% while using a round brush.

**Tip:** Just as with the synthetic hair wig, wash the wig in the evening so it is ready to wear the next day. Human hair will take longer to dry so you might consider alternating with a synthetic wig to allow for the extra air-dry time.

**PRODUCT KNOWLEDGE – HUMAN HAIR AND BLEND WIGS:** There are many good styling products made specifically for human hair wigs. Do not use products (including hairspray) containing alcohol, as the alcohol will dry out your wig and can alter the finish. To ensure the life of your purchase, invest in human hair wig-safe products found online or at a wig store that carries human hair wigs.

**Note:** For human hair or blend wigs, follow the manufacturer's care instructions and be sure to ask the retailer at the time of purchase for any helpful tips.

 SKINNY DIPPING

Need a wig you can wear while swimming, climbing into a hot tub, or participating in any kind of water sports? Some wigs are designed for high activity; others are more stay-at-home. Be sure to check on these options when shopping so you won't have to bare all on the beach.

## A NOTE FOR PERSONS RECEIVING CHEMOTHERAPY

As mentioned previously, it is not advisable to use wigs that require adhesives. Look instead for a wig with a built-in cap designed to allow swimming without requiring glue or tape. A custom wig with a cap made specifically for swimming may be worth considering. (For wigs designed for swimming, see Resources, page 151.)

**Remember:** Human hair wigs may not hold up well to repeated immersion in chlorine-treated pools or hot tubs. Finding a closely matching synthetic wig to wear while swimming may be the best way to extend the life of your human hair wig. Also, when wearing either a human or synthetic wig while sitting in a hot tub, consider wrapping a towel or a colorful sarong (bathing suit wrap) around your head.

**Human hair:** A human hair wig will respond more like natural hair, meaning it will temporarily lose its style after the wig is submerged in water or exposed to moisture, and will not look the same until you've had a chance to re-style.

## WIG WORKOUTS?
## DON'T SWEAT IT.

You may decide you prefer to wear a soft head-covering like a scarf or a hat when working out. There are hat and scarf wig combinations available as well, where the top portion is a scarf or hat and the perimeter is a wig. But if it's a wig you want, here's some advice.

**Vigorous workout?** If you typically shower at the gym, a second wig can come in handy. With excessive perspiration the wig lining can become damp, making it feel like your gym shirt after a workout. At the end of your workout, place your wig into a small waterproof bag so it is ready for you to wash later. The second wig will buy you some time and it will be comfortable and dry.

**Synthetic wigs at the gym:** A synthetic or blend wig can be used at the gym. However, like all wigs, it will hold in heat and intensify perspiration. Don't forget: no sauna or steam rooms for synthetic or blend wigs. Also, remember: do not blow-dry your synthetic or blend wig.

**Human hair wig at the gym:** Besides being hot for workouts, these wigs will tend to lose their shape after sweating or being in saunas, much like natural hair. Human hair wigs are safe for steam rooms and saunas, but I recommend using a towel or wrap to protect the wig's finish from the dry heat of saunas.

**Synthetic, human hair, and blend wigs:** These wigs may require more frequent washing, depending on how vigorously you work out. Keep a few bobby pins in your gym bag and a wide-tooth wig comb. Consider a pleasant-smelling moisture spray safe for synthetics or human hair to freshen up the scent.

## TRAVERSING TRAVEL

Here are some tips to make sure you
and your wig arrive in style:

1. Packing your wig? Turn it inside out and use a net
or wig cap to hold the shape.

2. Traveling to new heights? While on your magic
carpet ride, keep your wig in a watertight bag to
protect it from liquids or products that may leak at
high altitudes during flight.

3. Companion fares: Make sure you travel with your
wig-specific styling products and a portable stand to
place it on at night or after washing.

4. Staying grounded but ready to ride? With open sunroofs or convertibles, a scarf can be a stylish way to save the day. Also, you can use a few bobby pins for extra security. When tying back long hair, the scarf can be wrapped along the length of the pony tail, adding color and holding the hair nicely. A large pair of sunglasses will make your wig feel more secure, as well as protecting your eyes from the sun and wind. Keep a comb in your purse, as the ends may get tangled. Consider taking a travel-size moisture spray for longer drives. Now, you and your wig can arrive in style.

5. Always consider the nature of your travel and pack a few items like a travel-size moisture spray, a little mirror, and extra bobby pins to ensure your wig doesn't wander.

Many wigs have adjusters underneath—some are designed much like bra hooks—to help with a more secure fit. Once you have adjusted the straps to the perfect fit, take a cloth-style bandage and wrap it around the hook so the metal or hard plastic of the adjusters will not irritate your scalp. There may also be pressure points where the wig or wig cap feels too tight. To alleviate the pressure, try enlisting one to two pieces of cotton. The soft, flexible, and absorbent cotton will help keep the edge of your wig from chafing your skin.

### FOR ADDED SECURITY

Place a pair of bobby pins on either side of the wig, hiding them just above the ears. Secure the wig by sliding each pin through the wig and wig cap. This will enable you to loosen the straps to make it more comfortable. You might also want to consider purchasing a wig grip headband. This is a headband with an adjustable Velcro® closure designed to prevent the wig from slipping. You can wear this alone or on top of your wig cap. A variety of these can be found with a quick trip online or to the wig store. Wig tape, which can also be found online or at wig stores, can be used to help secure the wig. The tape is double-sided and attaches the wig to the scalp. Be careful around lace front or hand tied wigs so you don't pull out the hairs or fibers. Remember, I do not recommend adhesives for persons going through chemotherapy, due to skin sensitivity.

**CUSTOMIZED COMFORT:** In Chapter 2 (aka "Hairy Tales"), we talked about having a track of human hair sewn into the underside of a wig to make it feel and respond more like human hair. If the fibers of a synthetic wig irritate your skin, you may also sew in a strip of human hair—available at wig stores—horizontally at the base (or bottom) of the wig's underside from ear to ear to keep your neck more comfortable.

## FIT AND COMFORT FOR THOSE RECEIVING CHEMOTHERAPY

If you shop for a wig before hair loss, try not to judge the fit too critically, as it will fit and look different once your own hair has shed or been cut short, especially if you have long hair. I do not recommend shaving your head to the scalp, as it can cause sensitivity and ingrown hairs. Instead, use clippers with a guard, leaving a hair length of one-eighth of an inch.

*When you own your
breath nobody can steal
your peace.*

~ Author Unknown

# CHAPTER SEVEN

**THE ENDS**

FINAL TIPS BEFORE SHOPPING

**WHETHER** you choose to buy online or in a store, look for a large selection of wigs and make sure the return policy is clear.

# Breathe.

Take a deep breath and do your best to be patient. This is a process. It's something new, and like with most new things, it takes some time to adjust.

Shopping for a wig for the first time is a lot like shopping for a formal dress. Have you ever shopped for a dress for a wedding or special event? You may think you know just what you want, but often after trying it on you discover it doesn't look at all like you imagined. A first-time wig-shopping experience can be much like that. With a little patience, you will find the wig that is right for you. While it may not be quite what you originally pictured, it may well be better than you imagined.

# SAVVY
# SHOPPING

**COLOR:** Start out with a wig color that's flattering to your skin. As suggested in Chapter 2, when shopping, wear very little or no foundation to find the most flattering wig color for your skin, and look at the wig in natural daylight. Regardless of how attractive a wig may be, if the color is harsh or doesn't suit you, you won't look your best wearing it. When you find a wig you really like but you suspect the color isn't right for you, ask the salesperson for the full range of colors available in that style.

**COMFORT:** Put on the wig you're considering and take a moment to close your eyes and notice how the wig feels. Is it tight, heavy, hot, itchy, or is it chafing anywhere? Have you ever fallen in love with the way a pair of shoes looks in a store, put them on just long enough to see if they fit, purchased them on the spot, and found, three city blocks later, that the fairytale was over? Take a preemptive step here so your fairytale will be never-ending.

**MOVEMENT:** Stand up and walk away from the mirror. Swing your head from side to side. Does the hair move well against your clothes? What happens if it gets caught in your collar? Is it easy to remove naturally? The movement test will give you real-life experience with the wig.

**360:** Be sure to look at the wig from all angles. Take a hand-held mirror, turn away from the main mirror and look at the wig from the sides and the back. Once again, give your head a little swing from side to side, noticing the look and feel.

**EYEWEAR:** If you wear glasses or readers, like I do, you may find yourself occasionally taking them off to clean or readjust them during the day. Sit down in front of a mirror and try taking the glasses off and putting them back on and notice what happens to the wig. Is this easy to do or does it require readjusting the wig each time? Not in need of glasses or readers? I bet you wear sunglasses! Grab a pair from the car and try the same exercise to find a wig in an eyeglass user-friendly style.

**TOUCH TEST:** Do you touch your own hair often? Now is the time to see how your natural movements affect the wig you're considering. Touch the wig as you would your own hair (for example, move the bangs or front of the hair out of your eyes), and notice how the wig responds. Does it go back to its original shape or does it separate in a way that requires maintenance? Touching the wig should be something you can do without a second look or thought. Spend a little time performing the touch test; I want you and your wig to feel great.

**THE BIG PICTURE:** Wearing the wig, walk up to another mirror. Sometimes viewing a new look from a distance and then close up gives you a better perspective of the overall look. Like standing too close to the mirror in the dressing room, you need a little space to see the look as a whole.

**THE LITTLE PICTURE:** While trying on wigs, ask the salesperson if they permit pictures. I prefer the stores that allow this, as it's a great way to see yourself from a spectator's perspective. Also, if you are contemplating several wigs, the side-by-side comparison is really valuable.

**SALES SUPPORT:** Once the salesperson has seen you trying on a few styles, prompt them for suggestions. Like a personal shopper, these experts have seen many different styles and know what looks best on a wide variety of people. They know their inventory and can assist you by pointing out a wig that's very popular and may also work well for you.

**TIME:** Be sure to allow some time for this process. Sometimes, after trying on several choices, a wig you thought of only as a "maybe" may become a "yes" simply because you are now better versed in the way wigs look and fit.

# Once again, breathe. You've got this!

THE
PART

THE
HAIRLINE

When shopping for a wig, the most important areas to consider are the part and the hairline. Also, make sure the wig does not sit too low or far back on the forehead, but rather rests at your natural hairline.

 The 5 qualities to approach with caution are: LONG / STRAIGHT / THICK / SHINY / SOLID COLOR

 When deciding on a wig color, remember to view it in natural light.

 Shop for a wig wearing little or no foundation so you can judge how each wig works with your natural skin color.

 A few bangs or soft layers around the face will help conceal the hairline and add forgiveness to thinning eyebrows.

 Enlist a professional stylist who specializes in wig cutting to make adjustments to the wig while you are wearing it.

# SHOPPING LIST

- [ ] Wig Cap
- [ ] Wide-Tooth Comb
- [ ] Bobby Pins
- [ ] Small Mirror
- [ ] Wig Stand (for when wig is drying or not in use)
- [ ] Wig Gripper
- [ ] Waterproof Bag (for transporting wet wigs)
- [ ] Satin Pillowcase (comfortable for bare scalp or when hair is shedding)
- [ ] Head Covering (for when you are wigless)
- [ ] Wig Tape (for persons not undergoing chemo)
- [ ] Moisture Spray
- [ ] Hair Spray & Styling Products (alcohol-free)
- [ ] Shampoos
  (cold water soluble for synthetic wigs)
  (paraben-free for human hair wigs)

In addition to the pointers in this book, your most important asset on your wig-shopping adventure is a friend. A friend can buy or try on wigs with you. Having someone you know help you with this experience will give you more confidence in your choice, thereby offering a more enjoyable wig-shopping experience.

Stay tuned for more things wigs–the Appendix (just ahead) has lots of valuable information, including stories from patients, statements from oncology experts, and more.

*Now let's get wiggy with it!*

# ABOUT
*the*
# AUTHOR

Jeanna Doyle has worked in both medical and advertising settings as a licensed cosmetologist and a medical aesthetic provider. She has advanced training in oncology esthetics, skincare, and corrective makeup.

Jeanna's work has led her from Vegas to Venice, and many places in between. She works with actors and athletes, models and musicians, patients and politicians, as well as a former president and first lady of the United States.

In 2013, Jeanna started Suite HOPE (Helping Oncology Patients Esthetically)—a 501(c)(3) nonprofit—to help women with the appearance-related side effects of cancer treatment. Additionally, Jeanna has developed The HOPE Method—

the first internationally recognized corrective makeup training approved by the International Society of Oncology Estheticians.

Jeanna contributes corrective makeup and beauty articles for both medical and beauty industry giants. She also gives talks, often with live demos, for cancer patients, career-oriented women, and professionals in the beauty industry.

Jeanna lives in North Texas with her husband Brian Ruhl.

# *APPENDIX*

## STORIES, STATEMENTS AND STATISTICS

# THE COVER
# STORY

# Why Does A Book About Wigs *Not* Have A Wig on the Cover?

As we created the photos for *Wig ED*, I began to notice something wonderful. After each shot, as I pulled off the wig, revealing our model wearing only the snug wig cap underneath, I was struck by how beautiful she looked. It reminded me of why I love black-and-white photography. When an element–in this case, color–is removed, for me there is less distraction. With the wig removed from the model, I was looking at a beautiful face without a single distraction, not even hair. Then it hit me: this moment should be captured on film.

When we shot Ali Lagarde, I made sure to shoot her with the wig we'd planned for her, as well as wigless. The moment we began shooting her without the wig, I was certain we not only had a shot for the book, but we also had our cover! The image shows a beautiful face with a wig cap, symbolic of hair loss; but beyond that, representing the idea that any look is possible. I loved the idea of a book about wigs without a wig on the cover. Ali's wigless beauty frees you, the reader, to consider what look might work best for you. I've written *Wig ED* to show you how to find the perfect wig–and maybe more importantly–to remind you that if you choose to go wigless you are still beautiful, perfect, and whole.

# A SUITE STORY

How Suite HOPE and
this book came about

When my friend Ruth was diagnosed with cancer, she asked me where she should shop for a wig. I immediately volunteered to take her shopping. After our successful shopping trip, Ruth confided that if I had not gone with her, she would've felt completely overwhelmed by the experience. I realized that what was obvious to me was not at all obvious to Ruth. And then it hit me: there are probably many women who, like Ruth, might not know what to look for in a wig. Suddenly I felt this deep responsibility to share what I know about wigs. After all, my knowledge came from many years doing work that I truly love. The thought that I could now use that experience to help others was a powerful one that really motivated me.

*(continued next page)*

This began a journey that has led me to start a nonprofit called Suite HOPE (Helping Oncology Patients Esthetically). Suite HOPE's mission is to help women with the appearance-related side effects of cancer treatment. A desire to spread knowledge about wigs and the work of Suite HOPE led me to write this book.

After starting the nonprofit, I was interested in pursuing speaking engagements to help raise awareness about the important work of Suite HOPE. I asked a friend who works with presenters how her contacts got speaking engagements. She said, "They all have books," and then she laughed and said, "so you might want to write a book." She was joking but I was serious, so I wrote two books! This is the first one. The goal was to create a book that was both informative and inspiring; a book that would be a celebration of beauty, rather than a reminder of illness. One you might purchase for yourself or give to a friend.

With a mission to create a beautiful book that would be both easy to understand and enjoyable to read, I put together my dream team of photographer Tim Boole and graphic designer Chris Promecene. Now all I needed to do was attract a publisher. How hard could that be? Hard, as I would find out. It would be really, really hard. So much so that I did not attract a publisher. In fact, I was told by a literary agent I would need to self-publish.

# "THESE WOMEN ARE BATTLING CANCER AND THEIR HAIR IS FALLING OUT FROM CHEMO; PLEASE DON'T SUGGEST THEY SPEND HOURS SEARCHING THOUSANDS OF WEBSITES TO FIND THE ANSWERS THEY NEED IMMEDIATELY!"

I was asked, "Why is your book needed? There are thousands of websites on wigs." I replied, "Because none of them tell you what to look for and none of them are inspiring. Besides that, books are different; they are special, and there are NONE on this subject!"

The most important point I tried to convey to the literary agent was: "These women are battling cancer and their hair is falling out from chemo; please don't suggest they spend hours searching thousands of websites to find answers they need immediately!" I found it both ironic and futile to be defending the idea of a book, especially this book, to a literary agent. So instead I learned how to self-publish. This would prove to be both challenging and rewarding. Since the "a-ha" moment of shopping for a wig with my friend Ruth, I've discovered I am able to take on far greater challenges than I had ever thought possible. I want to encourage you to do the same; search for the potential within yourself that you can put to use to help others. As you rise to that challenge, the process may also change your life.

# NUMBERS
## *that*
# COUNT

\#

IF YOU ARE READING THIS
BOOK BECAUSE YOU ARE
EXPERIENCING HAIR LOSS,

# YOU ARE NOT ALONE.

NOTE THE SIGNIFICANT
NUMBERS THAT INSPIRED
THIS BOOK

\#

**CANCER STATS:**
Global cancer statistics for 2012 reported **14.1 million** cancer cases, with women numbering **6.7 million** (48%) of those cases. Cancer cases for both men and women are estimated to increase to **24 million** by 2035.

**ALOPECIA STATS:**
The National Alopecia Areata Foundation reports that **6.5 million** people in the United States are affected by the auto-immune disease. The effects range from hair loss in patches to complete hair loss.

**HEREDITARY HAIR LOSS:**
According to the American Academy of Dermatology's website, hereditary hair loss affects **30 million** American women. In quality-of-life studies, women experiencing hair loss reported a higher incidence of difficulties that interfered with their daily lives, including a significant loss of self-esteem, becoming introverted, feeling less attractive, and experiencing anxiety in public places.

**WIG AND HAIR GOODS STATS:**
Wig and hair goods in the United States and Canada comprise a 1.7 billion dollar industry. Further, 75% of purchases are made by women. More than 70% of wigs and hair goods are made from some form of synthetic. The industry has expanded considerably in the category of medical hair prosthesis (which may be covered by insurance), with numerous wholesalers now specializing in meeting the needs of medical patients.

# Donate your wisdom not your wig

If you wore your wig during chemotherapy, it is not advised that you donate your wig or allow others to wear it. The drugs used to help fight the cancer may be absorbed into the wig cap and may be toxic to others. If you would like to pay it forward, please consider sharing your knowledge, helpful tips (what worked, what did not work), a funny story, or favorite memory about wearing your wig. We have created a place to share your wig wisdom to help others.*

Please visit www.wiged.com and click on "Donate The Wisdom" to find out ways to share in and join the conversation.

RESOURCES:

**Cancer Statistics:** THE WORLD CANCER RESEARCH FUND INTERNATIONAL
http://www.wcrf.org/int/cancer-facts-figures/worldwide-data

**U.S. Statistics From:**
http://seer.cancer.gov/statfacts

**Wig and Hair Goods Statistics:**
www.wigindustry.com

*Consumer alert regarding the dangers of donating used wigs: Cheryl Coppola RN, MSN, OCN

# CONVERSATIONS
*that*
# COUNT

*Interviews by Jessica Scibona, LMSW*

"My sister passed away from brain cancer. It was terminal from the beginning and I was her caretaker. During that time, I was also diagnosed with breast cancer. I had a lumpectomy, yet did not tell anyone. Three years after she died, I was diagnosed again and it had already spread to my lymph nodes. I went to see a psychologist and he recommended Jeanna. I had come to terms with the idea of being bald and thought, *It is what it is.* I contacted her anyway and she prepared me for so much. She talked me through losing my eyelashes, my eyebrows—she made me feel so special and so loved... and helped bring me out of a dark place. My daughter was going to graduate and I called [Jeanna] to help me find a wig, as I was completely bald. We spent hours together shopping—she even drove me to get there. After she took me home, she called to say she had my perfect wig. She dropped everything to bring it to me. I didn't have a support group but Jeanna was my strongest supporter. She changed my life. She prepared me for what I was going to go through and she helped me face things."

— Amada

"Without Jeanna's help, I would have looked like a clown. We went to three different locations to try to match my hair color as best we could. Jeanna's help and tips made all the difference. She told me things I wouldn't even have thought to look for, such as look for something that doesn't have a part in it, as without one, you can style it better. She was absolutely right. I was able to tell such a difference and began noticing how big of a difference her suggestions made in how a wig looks. Wigs can also be very expensive. Everything I was finding in the magazines was over $150. With Jeanna's help, I was able to find something for less than $50 that I was so happy with. I got my wig cut and styled to match my natural hair and it worked so well. People did not even know I was wearing a wig. They would tell me I was so lucky to not lose my hair...they didn't believe me when I said I had! I know it doesn't matter to everyone but I didn't want to wear a thing around my head that advertised my cancer. I didn't want people to feel sorry for me. Having the wig allowed me to have confidence to leave the house and go out. It made me feel so much better. Even my family and my mother couldn't tell I had a wig on—it allowed me to have a life outside of my cancer treatment."

— Glenda

# "I DIDN'T WANT PEOPLE TO FEEL SORRY FOR ME. HAVING THE WIG ALLOWED ME TO HAVE CONFIDENCE TO LEAVE THE HOUSE AND GO OUT. *IT MADE ME FEEL SO MUCH BETTER.*"

"I didn't know anything about wigs other than what I had read on the internet. I found this shop and ended up buying a wig that was more than $4,000. Once I received the wig, I was not happy with it at all. I had read a few things like how chemo patients should not get human hair because of how much effort and work they take to style and maintain—this shop told me the complete opposite. I felt like they had manipulated me and worked me over to get the highest sale. I was put in contact with Jeanna and Suite HOPE through Dr. Kendall. My entire experience was so much different with Jeanna as she took me to a shop where we picked out a wig together. The shop clearly knew her and had a great relationship with her. I was immediately much more comfortable. Jeanna always felt like a friend I could trust. She helped guide me through the process and worked with me to find the best option that I would truly be happy with. I was able to find a wig with no stress, no pressure. Even more, the wig was less than $100. It's impossible to know what to expect with cancer. For women, you lose hair everywhere ... places that were once such a part of who you are—your eyebrows, lashes, and the hair on your head. Finding the correct wig helped so much with my self-esteem through the entire process."

— Pam

"In terms of my experience, Jeanna made it all okay. She was able to help with wigs and makeup. She understood what I would be dealing with through a process that was unpredictable and scary. She was able to stand next to me through my experience and prepare me for what would and could happen next. For a woman, our beauty is a big part of what we strive for. Your hair is a big piece of that, and losing your hair is a big deal. It's a very clear and real sign to the outside world that you're sick. I did not want that external label. Jeanna helped with color and what would work best for me and who I am/ who I was before cancer. She helped talk me through what a good wig should look like—things that never would have occurred to me. I was able to find a perfect wig in my price range that looked natural. People rarely realized that I was even wearing a wig."

"I WAS NOT PREPARED TO TALK ABOUT MY CANCER ALL DAY WITH EVERYONE I MET. MY FOCUS WAS ON LIVING, AND WHEN PEOPLE FOUND OUT I HAD CANCER, THEY LOOKED AT ME DIFFERENTLY."

"The wig allowed me to feel as normal as possible while I was going through treatment. I didn't want people to see my cancer. I wanted people to see ME. The wig allowed me to do that. I realize with some people, beauty is the least of their concerns when in cancer treatment. For me, it was about a life decision for everyone to forget that I had cancer so that I could continue to live and be me. Jeanna has helped make that happen."

— Ruth

# WHY WIGS

FROM FASHION AND FANTASY TO REALISTIC
REALITY, HERE ARE SOME WIG SHOPPING
STORIES FROM THE AUTHOR'S OWN EXPERIENCE.
THE STORIES AND PEOPLE ARE ALL REAL. THE
NAMES—AND SOME OF THE HAIR—ARE FAKE.

**IT'S A MATCH** I recently shopped with a woman looking for a wig who had her young child in tow. The child knew her mom was in the market for a wig, but did not realize it was because her mom had cancer. Imagine trying to shop with a child–wild with excitement–that is yanking wigs off the stands, urging us toward the most outrageous wigs available, and racing ahead at a speed only possible for youth. As I tried to stay focused on a believable and practical solution, a friend and her shopping companion stepped in to distract our little fireball. After several tries, we found a really good option. Suddenly, the innocent child appeared, looked up, and in a very sad voice said, "But, Mommy; that looks the same as your ***real*** hair!" In that moment we knew we had picked the winner.

**TEMPORARY WORK, TEMPORARY WIG** I met a woman through Suite HOPE and went shopping with her for a wig. She was in a temporary position and did not want to tell her employer that she was in treatment for cancer for fear it could affect her chances of being offered full-time employment. We found her a good match. I showed her the HOPE Method, which consists of techniques for recreating the appearance of eyebrows and eyelashes, and she was very happy to be able to continue her work with her privacy intact.

**THE POWER OF PRIVACY** I shopped for a wig with a wonderful woman who is a police officer. Yes, losing your hair can mean losing your privacy. We found a great wig that believably matched her own hair. It was a way to help protect and serve the very woman who was protecting and serving all of us!

**JOB WELL DONE** I worked with a woman through Suite HOPE who was between jobs, but was actively interviewing while simultaneously losing her hair due to treatment. We had a wig shopping deadline: whatever we bought needed to establish her look for the interview and throughout the stages of regrowth of her own hair. It was imperative that we find a great look that would serve her needs. We landed the perfect wig and she is on her way to landing the perfect job.

# WIG
## WISDOM

*by*
Amy Gibson

AMY GIBSON, EMMY-NOMINATED
SOAP OPERA STAR, INNOVATIVE WIG
DESIGNER, HAIR LOSS EXPERT, AND
AUTHOR OF **SEX, WIGS & WHISPERS**,
HAS LIVED AN INSPIRING LIFE, BOLDLY
NAVIGATING PREVIOUSLY UNCHARTED
TERRITORY (BOTH IN THE LIMELIGHT
AND IN CANDLELIGHT) WHILE WEARING
WIGS! WHETHER YOU'LL BE WEARING
YOUR WIG IN THE BOARDROOM OR
THE BEDROOM, AMY WILL INSPIRE YOU
AS SHE SHEDS SOME LIGHT ON THIS
SUBJECT WITH PASSAGES ADAPTED
FROM HER CURRENT BOOK.

As a woman who has lived with hair loss from Alopecia since the age of 13, I can tell you firsthand all the emotional turmoil and confusion hair loss and wigs can create. After losing all my hair at 30, at the height of a successful acting career, I was forced to create ways to keep my secret quiet through my 20+ years starring on soap operas for fear of being ousted from the industry as a bald freak and losing the only life I knew and depended on. Baldness was a shameful subject at the time that was never discussed. Dating was impossible, as books with insights such as my *Sex, Wigs & Whispers* did not exist; nor was it possible to get help about how to be normal in a world that worships hair. But a lot has changed since then...

Today, as an author, successful wig designer, founder and CEO of Createdhair.com, speaker, personal hair loss consultant, and cancer hair care expert for over 16 years, I have learned there is a better, easier way to live with hair loss and have fun with wigs. I am continually grateful to be able to help women and children face their hair loss journey with power and grace, and make wigs successfully work in their lives.

*Life does not need to stop because of wigs or hair loss. All you need are the proper tools.* You can still be social, work out, go out dancing, share beautiful intimacy, have incredible sex, and even SKYDIVE... all with your wig on. Yes, you heard me correctly. For *The Today Show* I jumped out of a plane, free-falling at 125 MPH without a helmet to prove how well my products work! (Learn more at createdhair.com)

Here are some words from my current book, *Sex, Wigs & Whispers*, that I hope you will find useful and inspiring.

## Feeling Good About Who You Are

Although it has taken some work, I've gotten beyond caring about what people think about my own loss of hair and wearing wigs.

If I feel good in what I am wearing and the way I am looking, then that's all that matters. I have made the decision and "created" my look and how I feel. I believe that the first person we need to make happy is ourselves. If we can do this, the rest of our life falls into place much more easily. I always say that "if I can get up and look in the mirror and know that I am doing the best I can for me, and I am living my life with integrity and respect for myself and those around me, then I can feel good about who I am." And that includes wearing wigs.

## Sharing Your Secret

When I decided to let someone in, it worked out fine. Largely because I took the time to get in control of my hair loss emotionally before allowing him access to my secret. This helped me keep my power and not give it away out of the need to "connect," which us many of us do who have lost our hair and a bit of our self-esteem or confidence. I wasn't looking for anyone's approval of me, another common behavior many of us fall into when experiencing hair loss. In my mind, he was lucky to have me!

Granted, it took some practice, but when I finally got there it was life- altering. And it can be for you, too.

As always, the decision whether or not to tell him is up to you. Do this on *your* time table. When it comes to your body... you are always the one in control. Remember, people react to information the way we present it. If we're in control, act as if everything is normal–so will they. *We are the only ones who give away our secret.*

One of the biggest lessons I have learned on this journey is, if I don't "future," and I just stay focused on what I need to do today to accomplish my goals for myself and my clients, then tomorrow is so much easier.

– Amy Gibson

# WORD DOC

THE FOLLOWING COMPELLING THOUGHTS ARE FROM FOUR OF THE MOST NOTABLE DOCTORS IN ONCOLOGY TODAY. PRACTICING AT SOME OF THE MOST PRESTIGIOUS CANCER CENTERS IN THE WORLD, THESE FABULOUS FOUR SPECIALIZE IN AREAS OF SURGERY, PSYCHOLOGY, AND DERMATOLOGY, AND ARE MAKING A DIFFERENCE BOTH MEDICALLY AND MENTALLY FOR THEIR PATIENTS.

## MICHELLE FINGERET, PH.D.

Associate Professor, Department of Behavioral Science
Director, Body Image Therapy Service
University of Texas MD Anderson Cancer Center
Houston, TX

Body image is a critical psychosocial issue for patients with cancer or any chronic illness that results in profound changes to one's appearance. These changes can be extremely upsetting, for both women and men, regardless of whether they are temporary or more long-lasting. Much research in the oncology setting indicates that having concerns about body image changes are normal and to be expected. Hair loss in particular is recognized as one of the most common sources of body image distress, with thousands of scientific articles on this topic alone. Despite the research devoted to better understanding the impact of hair loss upon a patient's physical, sexual, social, and emotional well-being, what many patients seek are practical resources that will provide clear advice and guidance to support them in their personal body image journey.

Such resources, to be useful and effective, must be developed by licensed professionals with extensive knowledge and expertise working within a medical setting. The information must be delivered in a compassionate and kindhearted manner, and must also be written in clear language that is easily understood.

"HAIR LOSS IN PARTICULAR IS RECOGNIZED AS ONE OF THE MOST COMMON SOURCES OF BODY IMAGE DISTRESS, WITH THOUSANDS OF SCIENTIFIC ARTICLES ON THIS TOPIC ALONE."

Jeanna Doyle has made an important contribution to the literature that can help patients who are struggling today with body image challenges related to hair loss. You will be hard-pressed to find another resource delivered in the same style and by a professional who is so passionate and eager to disseminate years of professional knowledge to others.

Thank you to Jeanna and Suite HOPE for all the ways you inspire, encourage, and help patients with cancer and for sharing your knowledge and expertise to all those struggling with hair loss.

**JEFFREY KENDALL, PSY.D.**
Director, Oncology Support Services
University of Minnesota Cancer Care
Minneapolis, MN

It is very common for people to feel self- conscious about changes to their bodies as a result of cancer and/or its treatment. For many cancer patients undergoing treatment, hair loss is often rated as their biggest concern. Research has shown that nearly half of all women considered hair loss to be the most traumatic aspect of chemotherapy and in some cases, women have refused to receive chemotherapy because of fear of losing their hair.

This fear of hair loss is a much greater problem emotionally than just vanity. Studies have shown that changes in appearance significantly impact a person's self-esteem and sense of identity. Self-esteem is negatively impacted because hair loss is a visible reminder of the life changes, the disease, and other stressors associated with cancer treatment. In addition, identity can be negatively impacted because women who have lost their hair due to chemotherapy report a near total loss of personal privacy because everyone else can see that you are getting chemotherapy.

"FOR MANY CANCER PATIENTS UNDERGOING TREATMENT, HAIR LOSS IS OFTEN RATED AS THEIR BIGGEST CONCERN."

Suite HOPE provides expert guidance, which allows cancer patients the opportunity to reverse the negative psychological effects resulting from cancer and its treatment. Rather than viewing themselves as victims of cancer treatment, women can be helped to feel empowered and embrace the opportunity to truly feel comfortable in their own skin and psyche. I feel Suite HOPE allows women to remain connected to who they are on the outside and thus maintain a sense of self.

Suite HOPE provides strength, hope, and connection.

## CAROLYN Y. MULLER, MD

Chief, Gynecologic Oncology
University of New Mexico Comprehensive Cancer Center
Albuquerque, NM

CANCER. It is not just a word that describes a type of illness where cells in the body become abnormal and grow uncontrolled, but it is a label that defines a state of non-wellbeing that impacts the body, mind, and soul. Although cancer itself may not be visible, cancer treatments often result in significant physical body changes that are visible—the most feared being alopecia, or complete hair loss. This physical change is viewed by many women as "the scarlet letter," as it is a curse or burden that is a physical announcement of the loss of one's health and the ongoing battle. Often oncologists and cancer care providers will focus on the treatments, the drugs, and the side effects that compromise major organ functions. In terms of the outward treatment, we tell our patients that the hair will grow back, and we prepare them that it might be different—be it curly, thick, or even gray. But those words do nothing to help women through the many days of lost self-esteem as a result of the visible loss of hair, eyebrows, and lashes.

Extensive studies prove patients survive longer and have an improved quality of life during and after treatment when a positive outlook is maintained. Best cancer care practices require a team of experts that can

"...EXTENSIVE STUDIES PROVE PATIENTS
SURVIVE LONGER AND HAVE AN
IMPROVED QUALITY OF LIFE DURING
AND AFTER TREATMENT WHEN A
POSITIVE OUTLOOK IS MAINTAINED."

work with patients to support all aspects of the mind, body, and soul. While many cancer centers have comprehensive supportive care teams, such as licensed spiritual and psychological counselors, physical therapists, naturopaths, and patient navigators, there are few trained oncologic estheticians like Jeanna to help with the most important impact of cancer care—physical identity. Our patients deserve the expertise reflected in this book, as well as the proper care and techniques to optimize maintenance of their personal self-esteem and identities during treatment and in the recovery phase. It is time we welcome Jeanna and her licensed colleagues to our teams!

## MARIO E. LACOUTURE, MD

Author, Dr. Lacouture's Skin Care Guide for People Living With Cancer
Director, Oncodermatology Program
Dermatology Service
Memorial Sloan Kettering Cancer Center
New York, NY

Many people lose their hair during treatments with either chemotherapy, targeted therapies, hormonal treatments, or radiation. Treatment administered orally or through a vein will make its way into the skin and hair follicles, affecting the way they grow and function. Radiation will directly destroy the follicles. Hair loss in people living with cancer has become an increasingly important issue. Since newer treatments are more effective than ever before, and devoid of life-threatening side effects, most people are able to continue their lives largely unimpeded during and after treatment. Maintaining an unchanged physical appearance contributes to their sense of self and well-being.

Hair loss during treatment is one of the most impactful side effects, as it may have an effect on a person's sense of self, whether at home, work, or school. Many people say they lose their privacy when they lose hair from chemotherapy, as it reveals they are likely undergoing treatment. We are currently investigating topical medications and devices that are applied onto the scalp during chemotherapy to prevent hair loss. Indeed, in December of 2015, the first device to prevent chemotherapy-induced hair loss was approved by the US Food

"HAIR LOSS DURING TREATMENT IS ONE
OF THE MOST IMPACTFUL SIDE EFFECTS,
AS IT MAY HAVE AN EFFECT ON A
PERSON'S SENSE OF SELF, WHETHER
AT HOME, WORK, OR SCHOOL.
MANY PEOPLE SAY THEY LOSE THEIR
PRIVACY WHEN THEY LOSE HAIR FROM
CHEMOTHERAPY, AS IT REVEALS THEY
ARE LIKELY UNDERGOING TREATMENT."

and Drug Administration for women receiving treatment
for breast cancer. Although highly effective, it will not work
for everyone, and many people may not have access to it for
various reasons. Therefore, *Wig ED* is critical to help you or
your family member choose and use the ideal wig that goes
along with personality, activity level, and budget. I have seen
many courageous men and women who have regained control
of their sense of self by choosing a wig that works for them
(many of whom are delighted by the compliments they get
from other people!). In summary, the advice in these pages
will help people living with cancer so that they can continue
to live life to the fullest.

Wig ED has launched an initiative to educate the next generation of hairdressers about wigs. Wig ED classes teach cosmetology students about wig construction, care, and selection. This is a program designed to insure that women will be able to get the information they need about wigs wherever they get their hair done.

**For more information please go to:**
www.wiged.com/beautyschools

# SUITEHOPE®
### HELPING ONCOLOGY PATIENTS ESTHETICALLY

Suite HOPE® (Helping Oncology Patients Esthetically) is a nonprofit that provides the education and support needed to empower women to address the appearance-related side effects that result from cancer treatment. With personalized training, women are able to resume their daily activities with both privacy and confidence.

Suite HOPE utilizes estheticians trained in oncology esthetics. The larger goal of Suite HOPE is to be part of an integrative approach to comprehensive cancer care by partnering with hospitals and cancer centers to bring this specialized service to all women with any type of cancer.

**For more information please go to:** www.suitehope.org

THE INFORMATION IN THIS BOOK WAS
ADAPTED FROM THE HOPE METHOD™, A
TRAINING CURRICULUM DESIGNED TO
HELP ESTHETIC PROFESSIONALS LEARN
HOW TO USE CORRECTIVE MAKEUP
AND WIG SELECTION TO ADDRESS THE
APPEARANCE-RELATED CONCERNS
THAT MAY ARISE FROM THE TREATMENT
OF CANCER, ELECTIVE PROCEDURES,
AS WELL AS CONGENITAL OR GENETIC
FACTORS.

For more information about offerings please go to:
www.thehopemethodtraining.com

www.facebook.com/wigedthebook

# WIGGY WORDS

A FEW WORDS ON WIGS TO HELP

DEFINE YOUR STYLE — THE ABC'S

AND W'S OF WIG WORDS

The following are terms that are useful for first-time wig wearers.

**Acrylic:** A kind of plastic or fiber made from polymers of acrylic acid or acrylates. Acrylic is resilient, takes color well, is washable, and is generally hypoallergenic.

**Alopecia:** Hair loss or baldness.

**Alopecia Areata:** A medical condition thought to be autoimmune in origin resulting in hair loss which may be in partial (in patches), or total (over the entire body).

**Beautiful:** YOU! Insert photo here. The definition of beautiful is you!

**Cancer:** Uncontrolled cell growth.

**Capless/Wefted:** Describing construction of a wig where synthetic or human hair is machine-sewn or hand-sewn into strips of material. These wefts are inter-connected in horizontal planes going back and forth over the entire cap.

**Chemotherapy:** The treatment of disease, like cancer, with the use of chemical substances.

**Clarifying shampoo:** A shampoo designed to remove build-up.

**Cranial prosthetic:** A hair prosthesis or cranial prosthesis is a wig used for patients who have lost their hair as a result of medical treatment or a medical condition.

**Fairy Wigmother:** Me!

**Fibers:** Material designed to resemble hair.

**Hairline:** The outline of the growth of hair on the head, especially across the upper forehead and temples.

**Hair part:** A portion or division of the hair that is separate or distinct.

**Hand tied:** Attached or tied individually by hand, not by machine.

**Heat friendly / heat resistant:** Able to resist heat in varying degrees.

**Hereditary hair loss:** Hair loss associated with a genetic factor.

**Human hair:** Hair derived from a human source; not machine-made.

**Lace front:** A type of wig construction in which the hair or fiber is tied into a light lace, used for wigs styled without bangs, allowing hair to be pushed back from the face exposing the hairline.

**Man-made:** For the purpose of this book, this refers to a type of wig that is not made from natural hair fibers but instead is made of a synthetic fiber.

**Monofilament:** The term monofilament, used in connection with wigs, refers to an ultra-fine mesh to which hair fibers, either human, synthetic or blend, are attached. It is virtually transparent, allowing the color of the skin underneath to show through.

**Natural hair:** Referring to the hair you were born with.

**Polyvinyl:** Relating to materials or objects made from polymers of vinyl compounds.

**Plastic:** Synthetic material that can be molded into shape while soft, then set into a rigid or slightly elastic form.

**Remy:** (Sometimes spelled Remi): Refers to 100% human hair with the cuticle of the hair intact.

**Synthetic:** Formed by a chemical process; not naturally occurring.

**Ultra fine mesh:** A fabric designed to look like your scalp.

**Vented:** Allowing for air to flow through.

**Wig cap:** A cap typically made of nylon to be worn under a wig.

**Wefted:** Describing construction of a wig where synthetic or human hair is machine-sewn or hand-sewn into strips of material. These wefts are interconnected in horizontal planes going back and forth over the entire cap.

**Wefts:** Ribbon-like strands of hair or fiber.

**Wig stand:** An object designed to support the wig when not being used.

**Wig warrior:** A volunteer who helps another through the wig selection process. Translation: A kind, supportive person.

# READING
# LIST

These are books that I think are both
useful and inspiring. Some are for facts,
some for fun, and some a little of both.

FOR THE LATEST UPDATES
CHECK OUT **WIGED.COM**

# Reading List:

For clickable links to these books go to: **www.wiged.com/reading-list**

1. ***Sex, Wigs & Whispers*** by Amy Gibson – destined to be a best seller, this book, just released last year, is part fascinating personal memoir and part advice on all things wigs, including dating and intimacy. This is a great book to read after you buy your wig, or even if you never wear a wig. I love Amy's wit, humor, and honesty. She has paved the way for both current and future wig-wearers, having worn wigs, on her terms, through more situations than most of us have encountered with natural hair. Amy also has a beautiful line of wigs and products. Learn more at createdhair.com

2. ***Dr. Lacouture's Skin Care Guide for People Living With Cancer*** by Mario E. Lacouture, MD, Associate Member, Memorial Sloan Kettering Cancer Center
Dr. Lacouture is the preeminent dermatologist with a special focus in oncology. Dr. Lacouture's book answers questions, addresses concerns, and gives cancer-related skincare advice. A great reference for anyone who has experienced any type of cancer.

3. ***The Girl With Nine Wigs: A Memoir*** by Sophie Van Der Stap – This is an internationally best-selling book. A moving look at Sophie's journey from cancer diagnosis at 21, through treatment and recovery. Sophie used wigs as a "cancer holiday." I enjoyed every word of Sophie's beautifully written book.

4. ***Raquel: Beyond The Cleavage*** by Raquel Welch – A New York Times Best Seller, this memoir, personally penned by Raquel herself, is a look into her life as a young mother, actress, international sex symbol and businesswoman. Raquel shares stories from her life and advice on beauty and aging gracefully.

5. ***Orphan #8: A Novel*** by Kim Van Alkemade – a novel based on historical events. This book, a New York Times Bestseller, was recommended to me because it touches on hair loss. I can't wait to see this as a movie. If you want a great escape and a fantastic read that's part historical but all incredible, read this novel.

# RESOURCE LIST

Friends old and new.
A list of resources from the author.

FOR MORE, GO TO
**WIGED.COM**

# Resources, Friends, and Faves:

1. **Bravadas Wigs:** Bravadas have beautiful stores offering privacy and professional wig stylists. Robinn Scholfield, the Kansas City store owner, was one of *Wig ED*'s valuable test readers. Scott Stark, owner of several locations, including Dallas, has supported both Suite HOPE and the Wig ED program for beauty schools. bravadas.com

2. **Created Hair:** Amy Gibson, contributor of the Wig Wisdom section of the *Wig ED* appendix, has long-term experience wearing wigs due to her own hair loss from Alopecia. Amy has created a line of beautiful wigs and wig-related products. createdhair.com

3. **Sally Beauty Supply:** I've worked with Sally Beauty Supply on everything from in-store signage to their signature magazine. Sally Beauty Supply stores sell beauty supplies that will be a wig wearer's best friend. sallybeauty.com

4. **Swim Wigs** (wigs designed for swimming):
**Amy Gibson, Created Hair:** offers swim wigs, swim wig tape, and swim-related products at createdhair.com
**Kim Karacz, Second Nature Hair:** Kim, who has alopecia, offers a custom line of wigs you can wear swimming or anywhere else. 2ndnaturehair.com

5. **Ulta:** A longtime favorite for everything from makeup and styling products to hair accessories.

6. **Wigmate:** Janice Henington, a cancer survivor, has developed a product out of her own frustration with Styrofoam™ heads and stands. Wigmate is designed to help you with drying and storing your wig after washing. wigmate.com

7. **Wigs.com:** Carliz S. Teague, one of the owners, has been a cheerleader for this book from our first meeting. Since then, wigs.com has also championed Suite HOPE and the Wig ED program for beauty schools. Wigs.com offers wigs, hair extensions, and video education. Whatever your wig needs, it's all there at wigs.com

# MODELS

ALI LAGARDE

ALI LAGARDE

ALI LAGARDE

ANDREA HAAG

ANDREA HAAG

CHIDERA OKONKWO

CHIDERA OKONKWO

LESLIE ALLEN

LESLIE ALLEN

CHLOE HUNDELT

CHLOE HUNDELT

LACEY BOLLINGER

MAURIE SMITH

MAGDALENE GROVES

ROXANNA REDFOOT

ALL MODELS ARE REPRESENTED

BY THE CAMPBELL AGENCY

www.thecampbellagency.com

PHOTOS BY TIM BOOLE, www.timboole.com

WIGS, WARDROBE, AND MAKEUP DESIGN

BY JEANNA DOYLE, www.jeannadoyle.com

# ACKNOWLEDGEMENTS:

**WORDS:**

I would like to acknowledge my technical editor, Trevor Riegelman, and beauty editor, Brooke Hollis Hortenstine; thank you both for your great insights and contribution to this project. To Gaye Weintraub, thank you for the lease ease and helping me get my copy right. Additionally, I want to thank the excellent team at FirstEditing.com for editing the book and offering additional peace of mind.

**PICTURES, POST PRODUCTION, & PRESS CHECK:**

This book was designed to be photo illustrated and that would not have been possible without Tim Boole, who breathed life into the images. Tim partnered with me on every aspect of this book–visual or otherwise–bringing the concepts to life. Thank you for laboring on all the details with me from image conception to press check and even helping with edits and marketing collateral, including the book's trailer and website design. You helped to check off every item on my wish list. You are insanely talented and I'm so grateful for your friendship, support, and contribution to this book.

**LAYOUT & DESIGN:**

I would like to express my deep appreciation for the brilliant cover and superb original graphic design provided by my long-time friend, Chris Promecene. I would also like to thank Jason Wheeler, who meticulously and elegantly crafted each page, many of them twice, for this first-time author. Thanks to Aaron Griffin for his excellent illustrations on pages 61-65. Thank you Ana Bohanan and Liana Cave for beautiful marketing support and website design.

**INSIGHTS AND INTERVIEWS:**

Dr. Jeff Kendall–the thoughts and perspective you provided in our section called Word Doc underscore how women are affected by this subject. Thank you for both your friendship and support.

Dr. Michelle Fingeret–your words moved me and your work inspires me; thank you for your contribution to this book.

Dr. Mario Lacouture–thank you for taking the time to provide your thoughtful words to the women reading this book; they are both powerful and supportive.

Dr. Carolyn Muller–with much love and many thanks for both your friendship and contribution to this project.

Jessica Scibona–thank you for your time and energy interviewing the courageous women whose stories will inspire and encourage others.

Amy Gibson–Amy, thank you for your wig wisdom–you said in your book *Sex Wigs, & Whispers* "...I have always believed that those whom I am supposed to help find me at the perfect time." Here's to the perfect time. Thank you for pioneering this path for so many so they too may live life fully, with or without hair, on their terms.

For Amada, Glenda, Ruth, and Pam - thank you for sharing your personal stories so that others may be inspired, like each of you have inspired me.

**THE MODEL AGENCY:**

The caliber of models used to illustrate this book would not have been possible without the support of my friends at The Campbell

Agency. Thanks to President Nancy Campbell, a long-time friend and cheerleader of this cause. To Peter John, who from day one believed in my vision and worked with me booking each of the models and helping me navigate the busy schedules of the beautiful models who worked to make this book possible. All the models are mentioned by name in our model index pages but to each of you, you have my deepest appreciation for bringing these illustrations to life.

**MARKETING:**
I am honored to introduce the team of women who have championed the cause this book represents. I offer my love and thanks to Annie Marie Scichili - you are a true powerhouse and a beautiful force of nature. Stephanie Bond - it is with deep appreciation that I acknowledge your diverse skills, which breathed life throughout the book and this cause. I'd like to thank my friend and board chair of Suite HOPE, Amy Green, AKA rinse and repeat. I am proud to call you friend. Jennifer Fomin - you championed this book and the cause from day one. Thank you for generously offering your time and talents, attending meetings, and contributing to the marketing, promotion, and message of the book. I am humbled by your contribution.

**PR:**
Many thanks to the amazing team of professionals at Smith Publicity, including Joe Papasso, Marissa Madill, and Sophia Moriarty.

**LIFE COACH:**
To Christine Clemmer for being a life coach, counselor, and friend. Your support helped me help others; I thank you with much love and appreciation.

**STYLE NOTE:**
The beautiful ivory dress in Chapter 1 was provided by Mario A. Gallegos Jr. at Petit Atelier Studio.

**TEST AUDIENCE:**
I would like to thank my excellent group of volunteer readers who pored over the book, offering valuable feedback to ensure the book is both easy to understand and entertaining. The group, which included both men and women, was comprised of oncology social workers, long-time wig wearers, marketing professionals, publishers, wig experts, wig retailers, and business executives; so basically, a group who knew much or nothing about wigs. Thank you!

Christine Allison, Stephanie Bond, Christine Clemmer, Jeff Cook, Catherine Credeur, Jennifer Fomin, Tracy Hobbs, Kim Keely, Kathy Maddocks, Brian Ruhl, Robinn Schofield, and Diana Statbucker.

**FAMILY:**
I would like to acknowledge my mother, Jo Doyle, for always living as an example in giving selflessly. Every kind and generous act you did helped shape this book and me. I love you!

**LOVE:**
Last and forever, I'd like to try to express my deepest gratitude to my husband, Brian Ruhl. You know I consider this book a love letter to the women for whom I wrote it; what you may not know is that I was able to write this book because of your belief in me, as well as the support and love you show me every day. I love you! Hey, book one just crossed the finish line. Next!

# INDEX